MAKE AND CREATE
SPOON ANIMALS
AND
PEN TOPPERS

Create a collection of fun characters!

Picture Credits: Includes photographs by
Photodisc, Corel, Ingram Publishing and Top That! Photography.

T̈OP THAT!

Published by Top That! Publishing plc
Tide Mill Way, Woodbridge, Suffolk, IP12 1AP, UK
www.topthatpublishing.com
Copyright © 2013 Top That! Publishing plc

Spoon Animals Getting Started

Get ready to turn ordinary wooden spoons into fantastic wild animals!

Just follow the illustrated step-by-step instructions to make a toucan, an elephant and a monkey. To make your spoon animal friends you will need a range of craft items, including coloured felt, goggle eyes, glue, wool and of course, wooden spoons! All of these items can either be found around the home or bought easily and cheaply from craft and hobby stores. The items needed for each project are listed at the beginning, so make sure you have all of the items before you start.

Top Tips

- Paint the spoons to match the animals' colour.

- Draw the shapes in pencil before you cut them out.

- Make the most of your felt pieces by cutting shapes out close together.

- Keep your felt offcuts to use for ears, eyes and noses!

- Remember, making great craft projects is fun. If you can't find any items try and think of an alternative, or why not try creating your own animal designs.

- If you run out of felt, you could use material scraps, coloured paper or paint to complete your animals.

- To make matching ears, cut one out and use it as a template to draw round.

- If you can't find any goggle eyes, simply use coloured felt or card in their place.

Tatu the Toucan

You will need:
A spoon
1 piece of white felt
A pencil and black felt pen
Glue and scissors
1 piece of black felt
1 piece of yellow felt
1 piece of orange felt
1 goggle eye

1. Place the spoon on the white felt and draw around it with a pencil, as shown below. Cut out the shape.

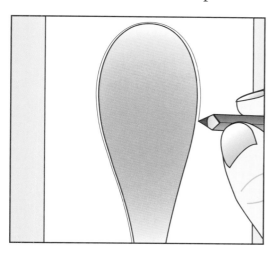

2. Place the white shape on the black felt and cut around it. Then glue the white shape to the flat side of the spoon.

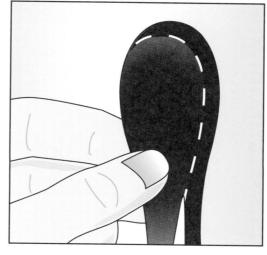

3. Cut a curve off the black shape as shown by the dotted line (above) and put the larger piece to one side.

4. Stick the smaller black curve on top of the white part of the spoon, as shown below.

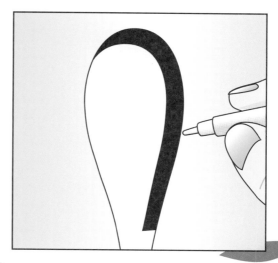

5. Shape the black felt you saved from step 3 into a wing, as shown right. Make small cuts into the lower edge of the wing shape for the feathers.

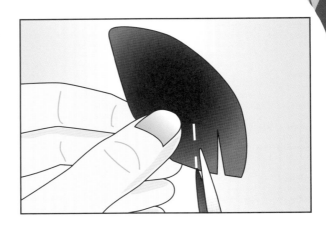

6. Cut a tail shape from a piece of black felt, as shown below.

7. Stick the tail in place on the spoon, and then stick the wing on top of it, as shown below.

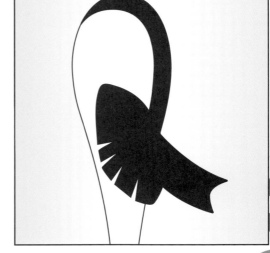

TOP TIP!
Use a piece of white chalk to mark out your shapes on the felt before cutting them out. If you can find tailor's chalk, this will easily rub off your spoon animals.

8. To make the beak, copy the shape shown right onto yellow felt and cut it out. Using this shape as a template, draw around it onto the orange felt.

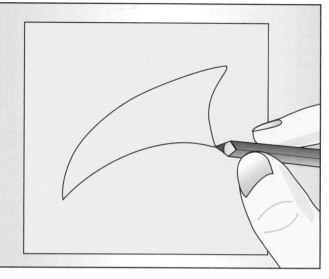

9. Cut out the orange shape, and then trim it down so that it is slightly smaller than the yellow one, as below. Stick the orange shape onto the yellow beak, as shown. Cut a small, thin strip of black felt and glue it onto the wider end of the orange felt. Stick the finished beak onto the face.

10. Stick a goggle eye onto a small piece of orange felt and then cut around it, leaving a narrow border. Stick the eye onto the toucan's face. To finish, draw a line on the beak with black felt pen.

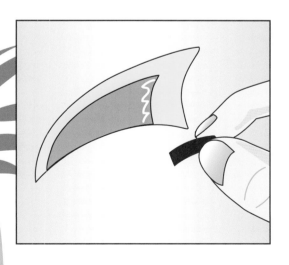

Ebo the Elephant

You will need:
A spoon
1 piece of light grey felt
A pencil and a black felt pen
Glue and scissors
2 pieces of dark grey felt
1 piece of white felt
2 goggle eyes

1. Place the spoon on the light grey felt and draw around it with a pencil, as shown below. Cut out the shape and glue it to the flat side of the spoon.

2. Now cut a piece of dark grey felt in half.

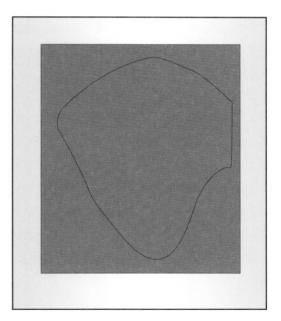

3. Draw an ear shape onto one of the dark grey halves, as shown above, and cut it out.

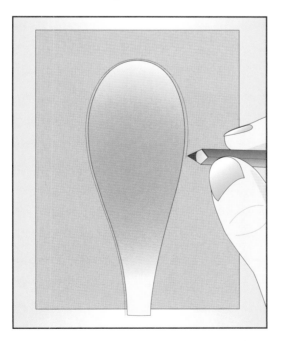

4. Using the cut-out ear as a template, draw a second ear on the remaining felt half, as shown right. Cut it out. Turn the spoon over and arrange the ears on either side of the elephant's head.

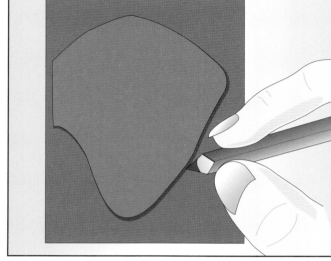

5. Glue the straight edges of the ears to the back of the spoon, as below.

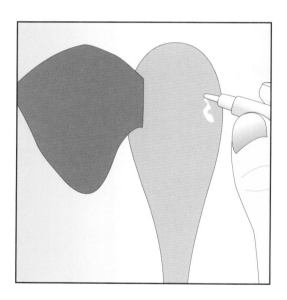

6. Draw the trunk shape, as shown below, onto the other piece of dark grey felt. Cut it out and then glue the top half of the trunk onto the front of the spoon.

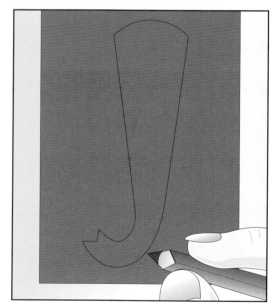

7. Draw a tusk shape onto the white felt, as shown right, and cut it out. Draw around this shape and cut out a second tusk. Flip one of the tusks over so that both curve inwards, and glue just the tops to either side of the widest part of the trunk.

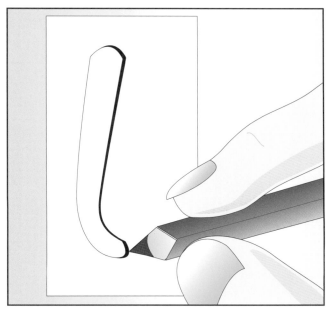

8. Glue the eyes onto dark grey felt and cut around them. Stick the eyes onto the elephant's face.

9. To finish, add some wrinkles onto the trunk using a felt pen.

Mumbo the Monkey

You will need:
A spoon
1 piece of pink felt
A pencil and a black felt pen
Glue and scissors
A pair of compasses
1 piece of brown felt
2 small coins, 1 large coin
2 goggle eyes

1. Place the spoon on pink felt and draw around it with a pencil, as below. Cut out the shape and glue it to the flat side of the spoon.

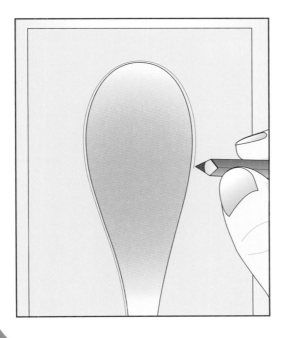

2. Using a pair of compasses, draw a circle, 5.5 cm in diameter, on brown felt and cut it out.

TOP TIP!
To make a circle, you could also draw round the base of a glass or bottle that is wider than the spoon you are using.

3. Fold the circle in half and mark out a pencil line, as shown by the dotted line right. Trim the shape along the line and unfold the felt. This will become the furry part of the monkey's face.

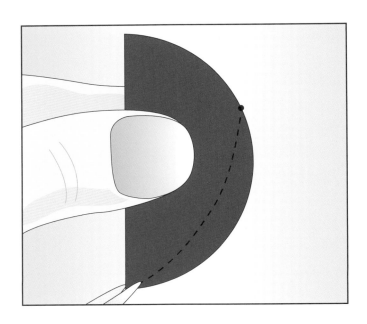

4. Place two small coins and one large one on the brown felt, as shown below, and then draw around the edge of the coins with a pencil.

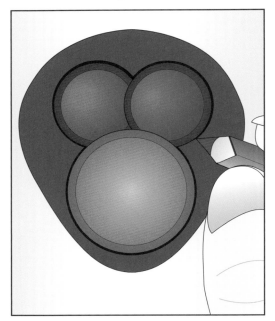

5. Fold the brown shape in half and make a snip in the middle. Unfold the felt and use this hole to place the scissors in so you can cut out your pencil line made by the coins.

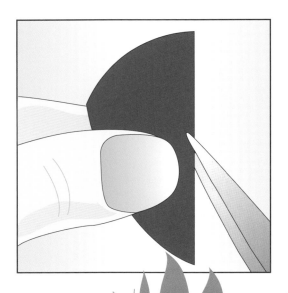

6. Carefully cover the brown face shape with glue and position it centrally over the top part of the spoon so that the pink area shows through. Now stick two goggle eyes onto the top part of the face, as shown.

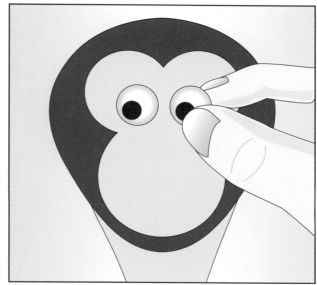

7. To make the ears, cut two circles, 2.5 cm wide, from the brown felt. From the pink felt, cut two circles, 1.5 cm wide. Stick the brown and pink circles together, then stick the edges onto the back of the spoon.

8. Using the felt pen, draw on the nostrils and the smiley mouth, as shown.

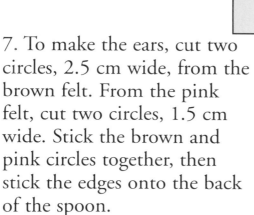

Pen Toppers Getting Started

There will be a party in your pencil case
once you've made these pen pals!

From a frog to a bee, a cat to a pig, the illustrated steps on the following pages make creating fun pen toppers easy! You will need a range of craft items which can be found in craft and hobby shops. Items you will need include pompoms, fuzzy sticks, beads, netting, goggle eyes and coloured felt, all of which are listed at the beginning of each project. You will also need some everyday items such as glue, tape and pens and pencils. Remember, once you have completed the projects on the following pages, you can have great fun creating your own pen toppers!

Before making your pen toppers, try practising the two techniques below on some spare craft items. This will make sure your finished projects look really professional!

SPIRALLING

Wind a fuzzy stick around a pencil to get a perfect spiral shape.

GLUING POMPOMS

Hold glued pompoms together for at least 30 seconds, to make sure they are stuck together.

If you can't find all of the items listed for each project, try thinking up fun alternatives to make the pen toppers your own!

FUNKY FROG

**Forget the lily pad –
Funky Frog prefers your pen top!**

YOU WILL NEED:

- black embroidery thread
- scissors
- 1 dark green pompom
- glue

- 1 light green fuzzy stick
- 1 dark green fuzzy stick
- 2 light green pompoms
- 2 goggle eyes
- a pen or pencil

1. To make the mouth, cut a length of black thread measuring 1.5 cm. Glue it in a U-shape to the middle of the dark green pompom, as shown.

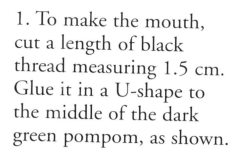

2. Now cut a 1.5 cm length of light green fuzzy stick and bend it into a V-shape. Glue it to the base of the dark green pompom to form the front legs.

3. To form the back legs, cut the dark green fuzzy stick in half. Bend and shape each piece so you have a curved shape with a webbed foot at the end, as shown left. The foot shape can be formed by folding the fuzzy stick back on itself.

4. Glue the bendy legs made in step 3 onto the base of the dark green pompom, with them sitting to the side, as shown right.

5. Take the two light green pompoms and glue a goggle eye onto each. Allow these to dry, and then glue the two light green pompoms onto the top of the dark green pompom.

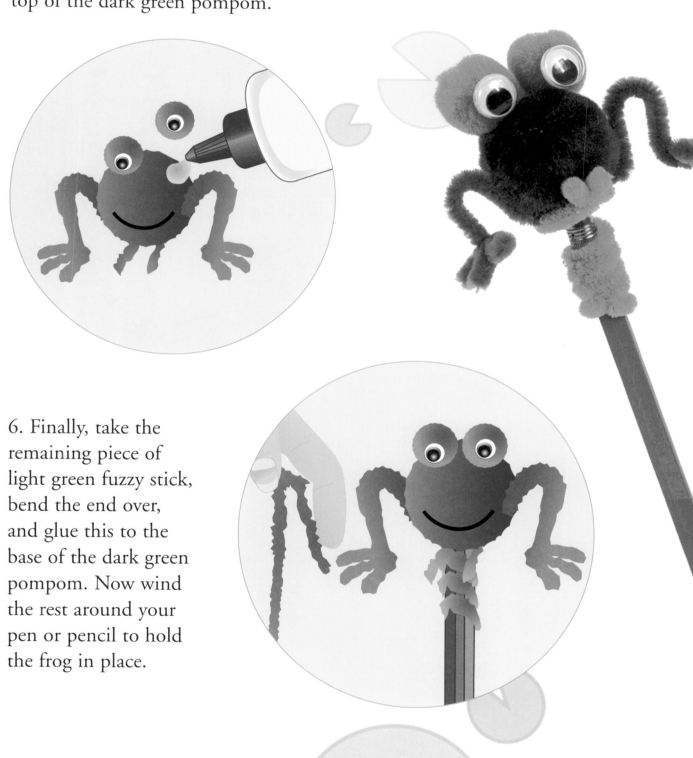

6. Finally, take the remaining piece of light green fuzzy stick, bend the end over, and glue this to the base of the dark green pompom. Now wind the rest around your pen or pencil to hold the frog in place.

Cutie Cat

If you know anybody who likes cats,
then Cutie would make a purr-fect present!

YOU WILL NEED:

- black thread
- scissors
- 1 medium brown pompom
- glue
- black felt
- 2 goggle eyes
- 1 brown fuzzy stick
- 1 large brown pompom
- a pen or pencil

1. To make the whiskers, cut six 1.5 cm lengths of black thread. Glue three on either side of the medium brown pompom, as shown right.

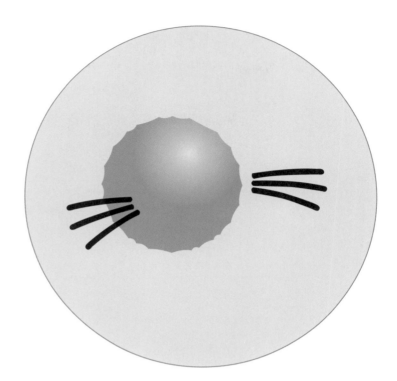

2. To make the nose, cut out a triangular shape, with sides 0.5 cm by 0.5 cm long, from the black felt. Glue the nose and goggle eyes onto the medium brown pompom, as shown.

3. Now cut out two triangles, with sides 1 cm by 1 cm long, from the felt. Fold each one in the middle to form a crease and glue onto the head to make ears.

4. Carefully cut the brown fuzzy stick in half. Curl one end of the fuzzy stick round, then shape the rest to fit the cat's body and tail, as above.

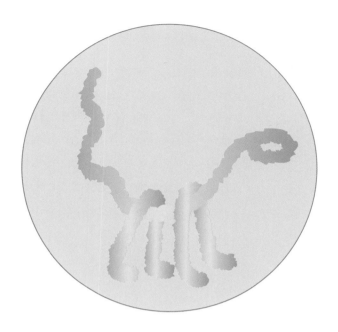

5. Now cut the remaining piece of brown fuzzy stick in half again. Bend the end of each piece to make four legs and twist them onto the fuzzy stick from step 4, to hold them in place.

6. Glue the large brown pompom onto the fuzzy stick structure made in steps 4 and 5, as shown right.

7. To finish, glue the completed head onto the loop on the fuzzy stick, as shown. To attach to your pencil, wind around the legs.

Buzzy Bumble Bee

Bzzz! Bzzz! Buzzy is so busy, he doesn't know what he's doing! It only takes eight simple steps to make him.

YOU WILL NEED:

- a small black pompom
- a yellow pompom
- glue
- 2 black fuzzy sticks
- a piece of netting
- a ruler
- scissors
- 2 goggle eyes
- coloured felt
- a piece of green felt
- a pen or pencil

1. Glue the black pompom onto the yellow pompom to make the head and body shape, as shown.

2. Twist one black fuzzy stick around the centre of the yellow pompom to form two stripes. Repeat this to make the stripes thicker.

3. Twist on the other black fuzzy stick where the stripes meet underneath to secure the ends.

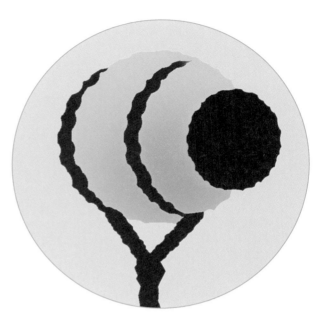

4. Cut a rectangle from the netting, measuring 7 cm long by 5 cm wide. Gather it in the centre and glue it behind the first stripe to make the wings. Glue the goggle eyes onto the black pompom.

5. Cut two small circles of coloured felt, measuring 3 cm in diameter – use two different shades. Snip from the outside into the centre of the circles to form petals, as shown.

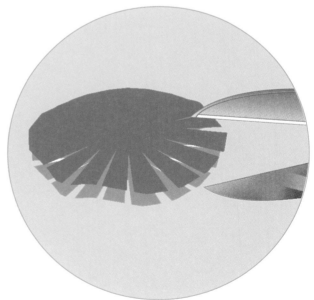

6. Carefully cut a hole in the middle of the petals and then thread them onto the black length of the fuzzy stick under the bee.

7. Cut a 5 cm square from a piece of green felt. Cut it into four leaf shapes, as shown.

8. Carefully cut a hole in the middle, then thread the leaves onto the black stem. Push the petals and leaves up against the base of your bee, then wind the remaining black fuzzy stick around your pen or pencil.

PERFECT PIGGY

This cute little piggy makes a perfect pen topper.

YOU WILL NEED:

- 1 extra large pink pompom
- 1 medium pink pompom
- glue
- a piece of pink felt
- scissors
- 1 small pink pompom
- a black felt pen
- 1 pink fuzzy stick
- 2 goggle eyes
- a pen or pencil

1. Glue the medium pink pompom onto the extra large pompom to make the head and body shape, as shown.

2. Make the pig's snout by attaching a small piece of oval felt to the small pink pompom, then glue this pompom to the front of the head. Use a black felt pen to draw on two nostrils.

3. From the felt, cut out two small triangles for ears and four trotter shapes (see step 4 for a guide to their shape). Glue on the ears.

4. Cut the pink fuzzy stick into four small pieces to form legs. Glue the four felt trotters to the ends of the fuzzy sticks and then glue them to the body, as shown.

5. Glue the goggle eyes onto the head. Finally, glue a fuzzy stick to the base of the pig's body. Wind the fuzzy stick around a pen or pencil once the glue is dry.